CAT on the RUN

EPiSODE 1

CAT OF DEATH!

Published in the UK by Scholastic, 2023
1 London Bridge, London, SE1 9BG
Scholastic Ireland, 89E Lagan Road, Dublin Industrial Estate, Glasnevin, Dublin, D11 HP5F

SCHOLASTIC and associated logos are trademarks and/or
registered trademarks of Scholastic Inc.

First published in Australia by Scholastic Australia, 2023

Text and illustrations © Aaron Blabey, 2023
Designed by Nicola Stofberg

The right of Aaron Blabey to be identified
as the author and illustrator of this work has been asserted by them
under the Copyright, Designs and Patents Act 1988.

ISBN 978 07023 2996 8

A CIP catalogue record for this book is available from the British Library.

Printed by Bell and Bain Ltd, Glasgow.

1 3 5 7 9 10 8 6 4 2

www.scholastic.co.uk

A SCHOLASTIC PRESS BOOK FROM SCHOLASTIC AUSTRALIA

AARON BLABEY

CAT on the RUN

EPISODE 1

CAT OF DEATH!

BOB33
#bestthingiveeverseen

LUCYBANANAS
HILARIOUS

RICKYMAC2
I love her so much!!!

DAISYD
Stop it! It hurts!

LIKES
3,165,002,711

ANDYWHACK
HAHAHAHAHA

KITTYFOREVER
Funniest thing EVER

SUNLI909
This is why the internet is good

ZIPPITYDOO
LOVE! LOVE! LOVE!

LIKES
3,352,308,922

BONKERSJOE
She's the best

MILLYWOO
PRINCESS FOREVER!

HOTDIGGITY
I could watch that all day

NEVERSAYNEVER
Funny stuff. OMG.

WAKAWAKA
LOL!

LIKES
3,511,984,777

LIKES
3,712,002,137

Are you sure about this?

Oh,
yes.

Princess BEAUTiFUL

Princess Beautiful
2.2 billion subscribers

Boogie Woogie Kitty

2.7 billion views

Bread Head

2.3 billion views

Hang In There!

3.3 billion views

Box O' Trouble

2.9 billion views

THE WORLD'S #1 CAT VIDEO STAR!

VID-E-GRAM CHANNEL

Screen Door Capers

2.8 billion views

Uh-Oh

3.1 billion views

The Chips Are Down

3.7 billion views

Cucumber Freak Out

3.1 billion views

She's perfect . . .

The World's Favourite Kitty
3,855,002,351 views

. . . absolutely *perfect*.

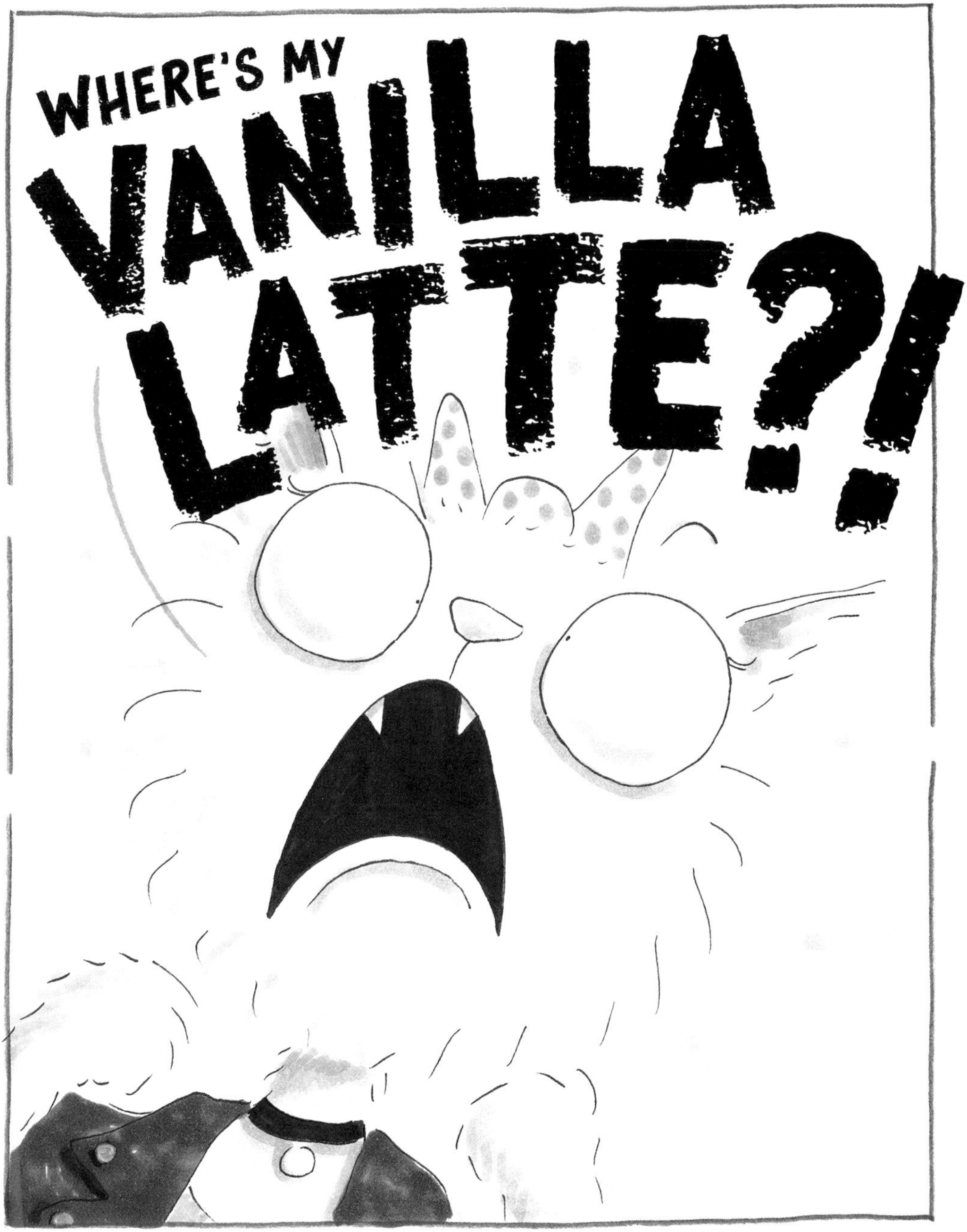
WHERE'S MY
VANILLA
LATTE?!

One
#1 AIN'T EASY

IT'S HERE,
MS BEAUTIFUL!
IT'S HERE!

Princess, we REALLY do need to talk sweaters. For the **VIDEO SHOOT**.

BRICK, not now. I'm too overwhelmed. About *tonight*.

OMG! **DATE NIGHT!**

I can't COPE.

Have you *seen* this . . . ?

In fact, DEVON, why are you giving me VANILLA LATTES?!

I NEED TO CLEANSE!

Because you look great and you asked me for one . . .

FLING!

GET ME A GREEN TEA! MY BODY IS A TEMPLE!

3 BILLION?!

THREE?!

Okaaay, Ms Beautiful!
It's LASER TIME!
You GOT this. And . . . *GO!*

RED DOT!

I NEED MY
PERSONAL TRAINER
AND I NEED HIM NOW!

RUSTY!
Where ARE you?!

Ahhh . . . I could *maaaaaaaaaybe* do 5pm tomorrow evening, Ms Beautiful . . .

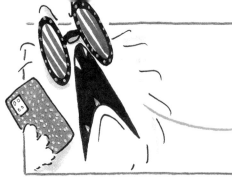

NO!
YOU CAN DO
NOW!

*I'M ON
MY WAY!*

VIDEO STUDIO

Anyhoo . . .
I was saying . . .
today we're doing
another of your hilarious
TYPING CAT VIDEOS.
You'll be wearing a
super cute sweater . . .

FLOP!

Adorable.

And **LARRY** over here will be under the table, making your arms go up and down as you pretend to . . . er . . . type.

It's an honour, Ms Beautiful.

It'll be another guaranteed **CROWD-PLEASER,** I'm sure you'd agree.

LOOK AT THIS!

LQ
The Enlightened
BILLIONAIRE HEIR
(with Hella...

CATRICK rebuilds villages.

CATRICK cures diseases.

CATRICK has photo sessions with, like, **OLD MONKS** and stuff . . .

AND NOW LOOK AT *ME!* **WHAT DO YOU SEE?!**

The
BIGGEST STAR
IN THE WORLD.

Who **EVERYONE** loves.

And look – you're now so popular, they've officially changed the word 'TRENDING' to

'PRINCESSING'.

That's what everyone loves.

But don't you see?! There's *MORE TO ME THAN* **THIS?!** There really is . . .

I HAVE HIDDEN LAYERS!

Hmmm . . .

Two
THE FUSE IS LIT

FILMING IN PROGRESS

OK!
QUIET ON SET!
'Hilarious cat video' #412.
Uh, take #1 . . .
Here we go . . . again.

Is that OK,
Ms Beautiful?

Oh yeah, it's
great, Larry.
They can just
hand me the

**NOBEL
PRIZE**

right now . . .

Yes, actually.

Awesome.

And, anyway,
I just wanted to drop by
and tell you how much
I'm looking forward to . . .

You are SO loved . . .
by the
WHOLE WORLD.

That's a very special thing.

I feel very lucky to
know you, Princess.

Wake up, Larry.
It's your time to shine.

KA-
FLOP!

WHAT
ARE WE
WAITING
FOR?!

Hmmm, scorpions. *Delicious.* That thang is makin' me hungry . . .

DEVON! I NEED A LUNCH RESERVATION!

AND . . . ACTION!

And THAT is why she's #1.

AND . . .
CUT!

And . . .
POSTING
on ALL social
media platforms.

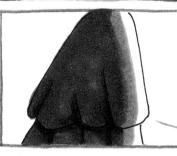

Zoom in on her computer screen.

WARNING
SECURITY
BREACH

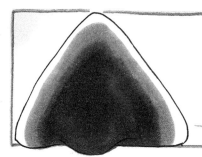

And now **REPOST** it on her popular little channel . . .

DANGER!
DANGER!

CLICK!

...TIVATED

...MENTS

...AT?!

...'t understand.

...a joke?
...FUNNY!

...neone explain
...e?

WARNING!

COMMENTS

Why is Princess Beautiful downloading Nuclear Launch Codes?

#freakingout

Is this real?! Is this a real thing? #realthing?!

DO NOT PROCEED!

COMMENTS

What is going on with Princess Beautiful?!

#HUH?

I'm a bit scared.

Is anyone else a bit scared?

...ES
...D!

...h

DANGER! DANGER!

COMMENTS

PRINCESS BEAUTIFUL?!

It's a HOAX. Must be a HOAX.

Looks kind of real to me.

What is happening?!

SECURITY BREACH

COMMENTS

Princess Beautiful has crossed the line.

#heartbroken

It's a CAT VIDEO. Let's stay calm, people.

Weird video, dude.

**WA...
DA...**

COMMENT...

This is mak...

I thought th...

Princess Bea...

#notfunny

#reallynotfunr...

Good morning,
I'm **CHUCK MELON**
and this is Channel 6
ACTION NEWS . . .

SPECIAL REPORT

6 *NEWS* **CHUCK MELON**

DISTURBING FOOTAGE

has been posted online by a famous 'Cat Video' star . . .

The alarming video shows that the
CRAZED-LOOKING
feline celebrity appears to be downloading
NUCLEAR LAUNCH CODES
and
ARMING NUCLEAR MISSILES.

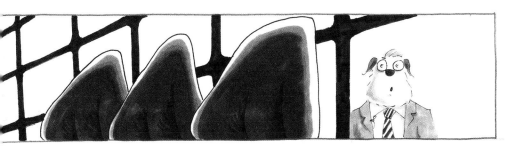

If you hear Incident Reponse Sirens in your city,

IT IS NOT A DRILL.

MORE UPDATES AFTER THIS COMMERCIAL BREAK.

SECURITY

COMING THROUGH!
This is an emergency!
I'm a PERSONAL TRAINER!

Three
WILD FIRE

THE

END OF THE WORLD?!

A **6** *NEWS* SPECIAL REPORT

And here with further
SHOCKING DEVELOPMENTS
in the potential

NUCLEAR-**CAT**ASTROPHE,
our on-the-spot reporter
TIFFANY FLUFFIT-

Thanks, Chuck!
Here on my phone is a
LAUGH-A-MINUTE
CAT VIDEO . . .

And here behind me – a building that looks like a **NUCLEAR SILO** that COULD contain **WORLD-ENDING NUCLEAR MISSILES!**

What do these two things **HAVE IN COMMON?**

PRINCESS

PRINCESS BEAUTIFUL,

that's what.

Yes, the world's

#1 CAT VIDEO STAR,

red-carpet fixture and
MEOW Magazine's
#3 Best Dressed Cat

HAS GONE ROGUE.

Details are scarce at the moment . . . but who needs details when you have

SOCIAL MEDIA BACKLASH

like . . .

THIS!

COMMENTS

That cat is evil!

She's a psychopath and must be stopped!

I never liked her!

I don luk thad cat

I loved her and now I HATE HER SO MUCH!

#CATFACEDWORLDENDER

#NEVERLIKEDHER

The **ARMED FORCES** are scrambling jets . . .

and rolling out an unprecedented

GROUND RESPONSE.

But with cities already in **CHAOS**, is it all too little, too late?

BWAAAAAAAARP!
BWAAAAAAAAAAAARP!

The question now, Chuck –

IS WILL SHE KILL US ALL?!

Whatever you do . . .
DON'T PANIC.

YOU RUN,
GIRLFRIEND!

YOU CAN MAKE IT!
I DON'T KNOW
YOUR REASONS FOR
ENDING THE WORLD,
BUT I'M SURE THEY
ARE VERY GOOD.

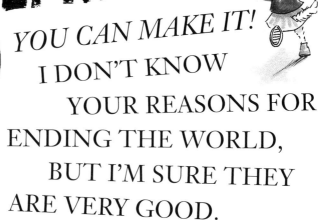

RUN!

THEY'LL NEVER CATCH YOU!

CAUGHT!

Four

TRIAL BY INTERNET...

THE
CAT OF DEATH
HAS BEEN APPREHENDED!

POLI

LIVE! LIVE! LIVE!

BREAKING!　6 NEWS

In a **RECORD-BREAKING DECISION,**
the JURY moved to convict the
disgraced INTERNET STAR in less than
13 SECONDS.

The JUDGE'S sentencing
was equally swift.

Good morning.
1000 YEARS!

What were her
MOTIVES?
We may never know.

But when the
INTERNET
turns on you that fast, Chuck,
YOU MUST
BE GUILTY.

MOTIVES, SCHMOTIVES.

The people have
SPOKEN.

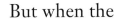

In fact, many have
questioned how she
managed to go
undetected for so long . . .

She's **EVIL!** Plain and simple.

Just look at those videos! She's a **MANIAC!**

No **NORMAL** cat would act that way.

I just don't like her. I just **DON'T.**

And in a **CHANNEL 6 EXCLUSIVE,** here's what those **CLOSEST TO HER** had to say . . .

As for her latest beau, **CATRICK CASH** – SON and HEIR to TRILLIONAIRE MEDIA MOGUL **THADDEUS CASH** –

he has made himself unavailable for comment.

Sources close to Cash say he is – quote –'DEVASTATED' by the verdict and has vowed to **PROVE HER INNOCENCE.**

Good luck
with THAT, buddy.

But perhaps the last word should go to her **STYLIST-**

Well, she told us she had **HIDDEN DEPTHS** but who could have possibly known what THAT meant?

I mean . . . *OMG.*

SPECIAL REPORT

6 *NEWS*   ARTISAN STYLE GURU **BRICK SAUVIGNON**

Five
OFF TO THE BIG HOUSE

Sir?

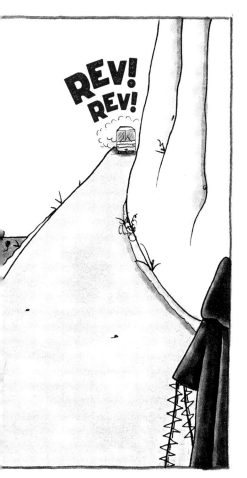

Why is this *happening to me?*

Can you imagine if someone THIS dangerous got loose, Phil?!

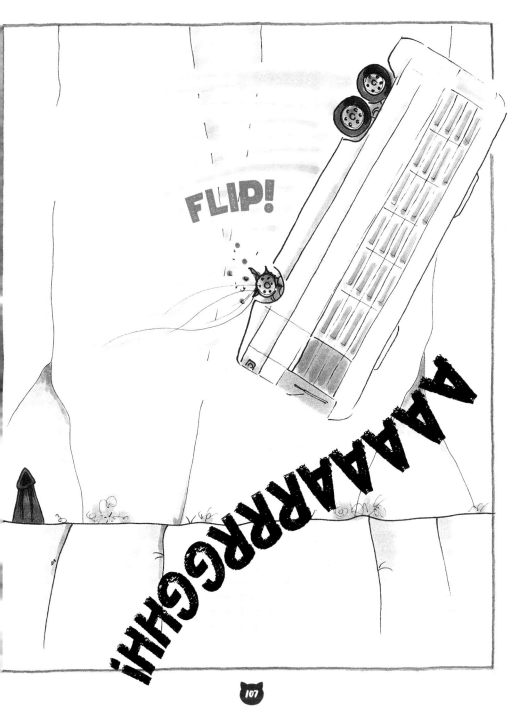

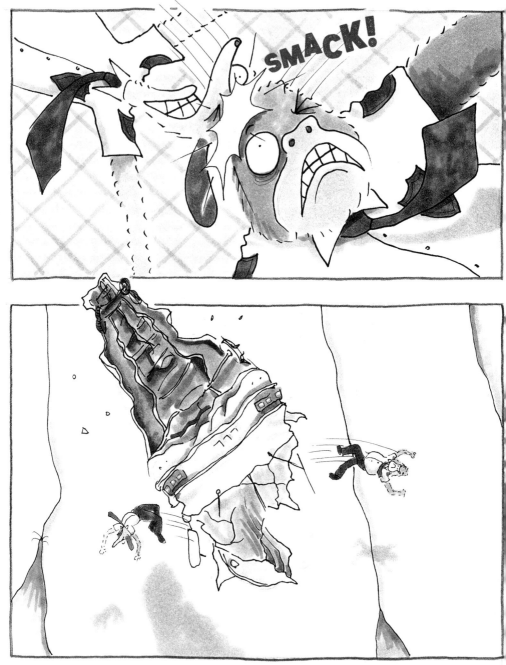

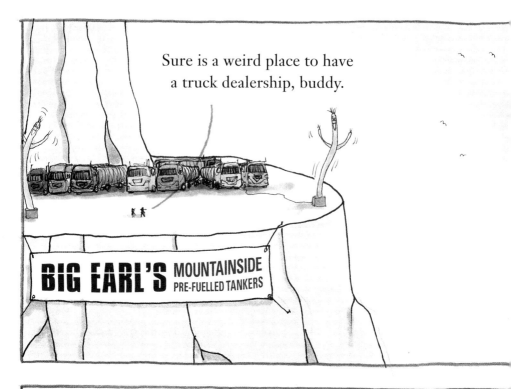

Sure is a weird place to have
a truck dealership, buddy.

Well now, that's what
makes us famous . . .

THAT and the fact that I sell these tankers **PRE-FUELED TO THE BRIM** with **FLAMMABLE LIQUIDS.** All 70 of these rigs are carrying 10,000 gallons of **HIGH-OCTANE FUEL.**

SSSSSS!

Well, I'll be . . .

At least the
prison is still
in one piece.

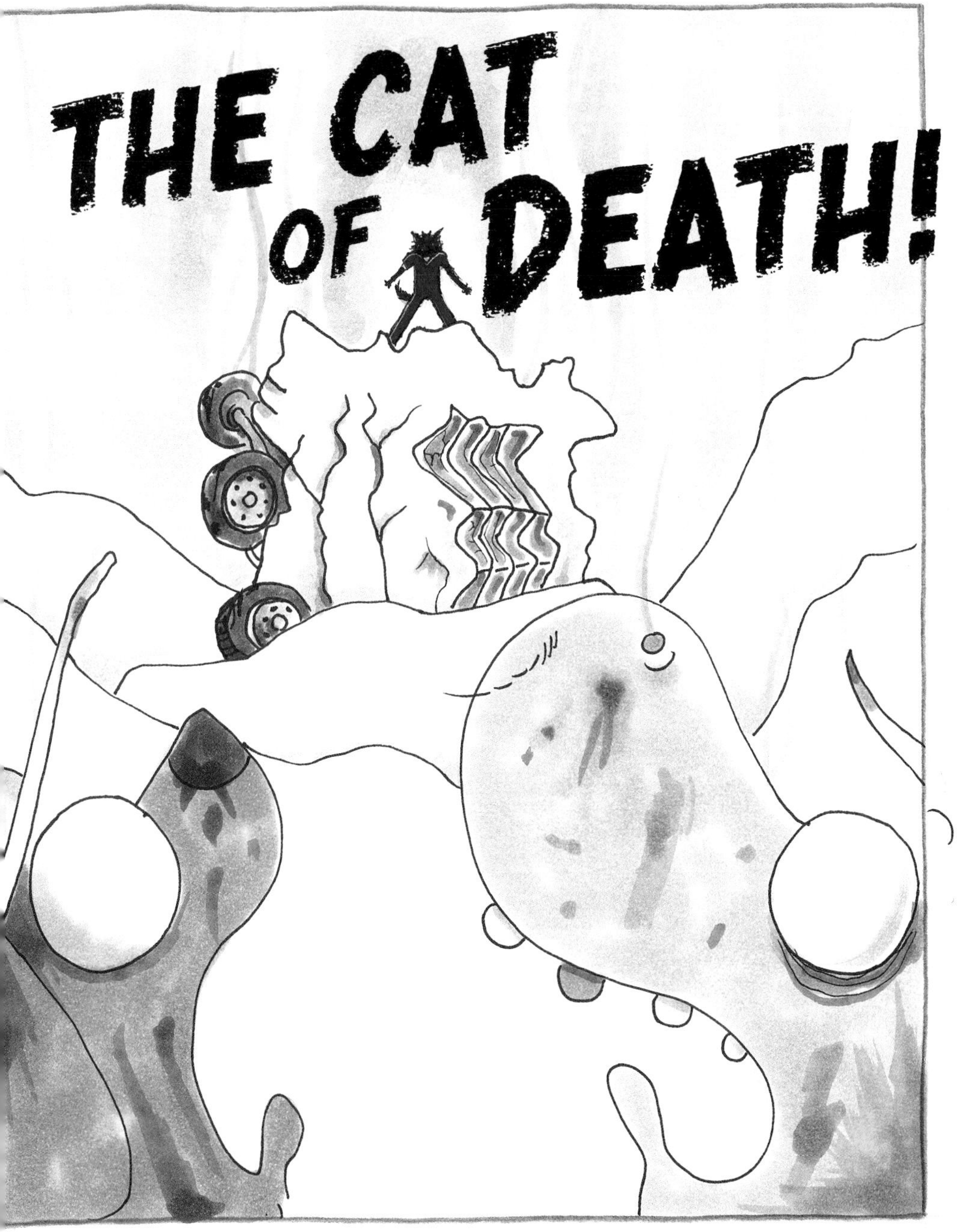
THE CAT OF DEATH!

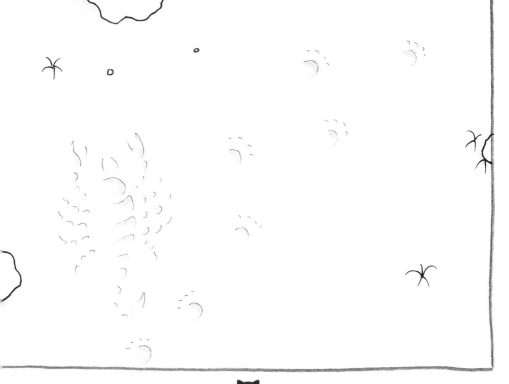

THE CHEESEMAN COMETH

Six

It's the **WORST CASE SCENARIO!**

ESCAPE!

She's LOOSE!
And it would be unethical
of me to deny that
NOW WE'RE ALL
PROBABLY
GOING TO DIE!

SPECIAL REPORT

6 NEWS **TIFFANY FLUFFIT**

Unsurprisingly, the internet is **ABLAZE.**

KA-BOOM!

COMMENTS

Look at what's she's done! MONSTER!

I fear for the future!

Weird place for a truck dealership though.

skingforit

COMMENTS

#fearfearfear

#somuchfear

#fearontoast

THIS IS THE END

I hate her typing face.

COMMENTS

Look at her eyes!

That is totally photoshopped.

Disbeliever! Those are her eyes!

#REDEYESAREREAL

Here are the lucky few who **MIRACULOUSLY** escaped with their lives . . .

And then her eyes went RED and she flipped the bus over *with her mind.*

SPECIAL REPORT

6 NEWS

PRISON BUS DRIVER **STU WOCKACHOWSKY**

Missy, it's only a matter of time before she gets her hands on another computer and **LAUNCHES THEM MISSILES.** This is as serious as a *heart attack*.

So take a GOOD LOOK at the **FACE OF EVIL.**

No stranger to topping lists . . . she's **#1** again but this time it's for being **MOST WANTED BY THE LAW!**

1. PRINCESS
BEAUTIFUL

2. MR WOLF

3. MR SNAK

F. B. I

10 MOS
WANTE

5. MR PIRANHA

TICK, TOCK!
HOW LONG BEFORE SHE STRIKES AGAIN?!

Alright!
LISTEN UP!

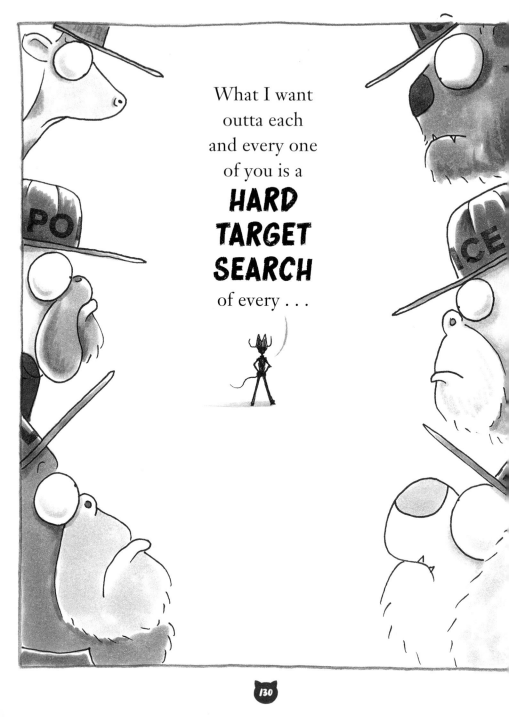

What I want
outta each
and every one
of you is a

**HARD
TARGET
SEARCH**

of every . . .

henhouse,
cat's house,
dog's house . . .

basically, any kind of
animal's house . . .

within a
**TEN MILE
RADIUS.**

CRASH
SITE

5

10

Seven

SHE WALKS AMONG US

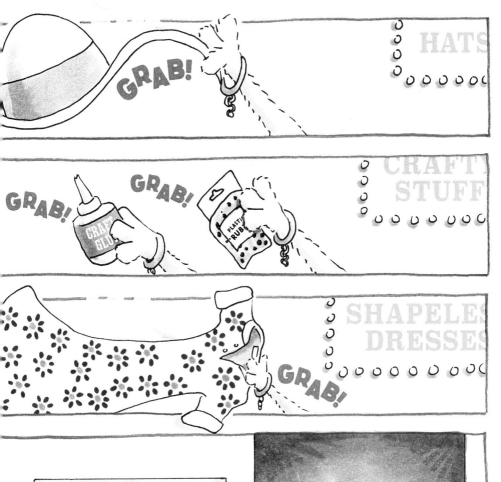

FITTING
ROOMS

Girl, you done *lost your mind.*

FITTIN
ROOM

Well, if *that's* the kind of service you get outside the city . . .

OK, focus . . . *you can do this.*

In fact, this is *easy*.
Remember, you run a

MULTI-PLATFORM ENTERTAINMENT ORGANISATION.

THAT'S
hard.

THIS is easy because . . .

. . . you didn't do anything wrong. You didn't do anything but make people laugh by filming a billion stupid videos. You DID NOT try to launch nuclear weapons.

You just have to PROVE it.

Now, *think* . . .

What do you have to go on?

FFFFF!

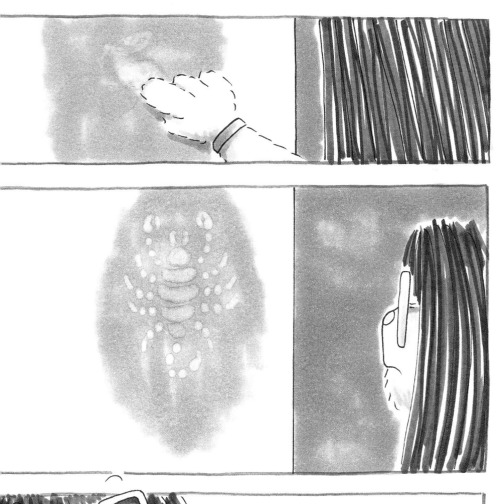

That has to mean
something . . .

But *what*?

One final
touch . . .

OK.
You're ready.

And just
remember . . .

. . . with this
disguise,
NO-ONE
will EVER
recognise you.

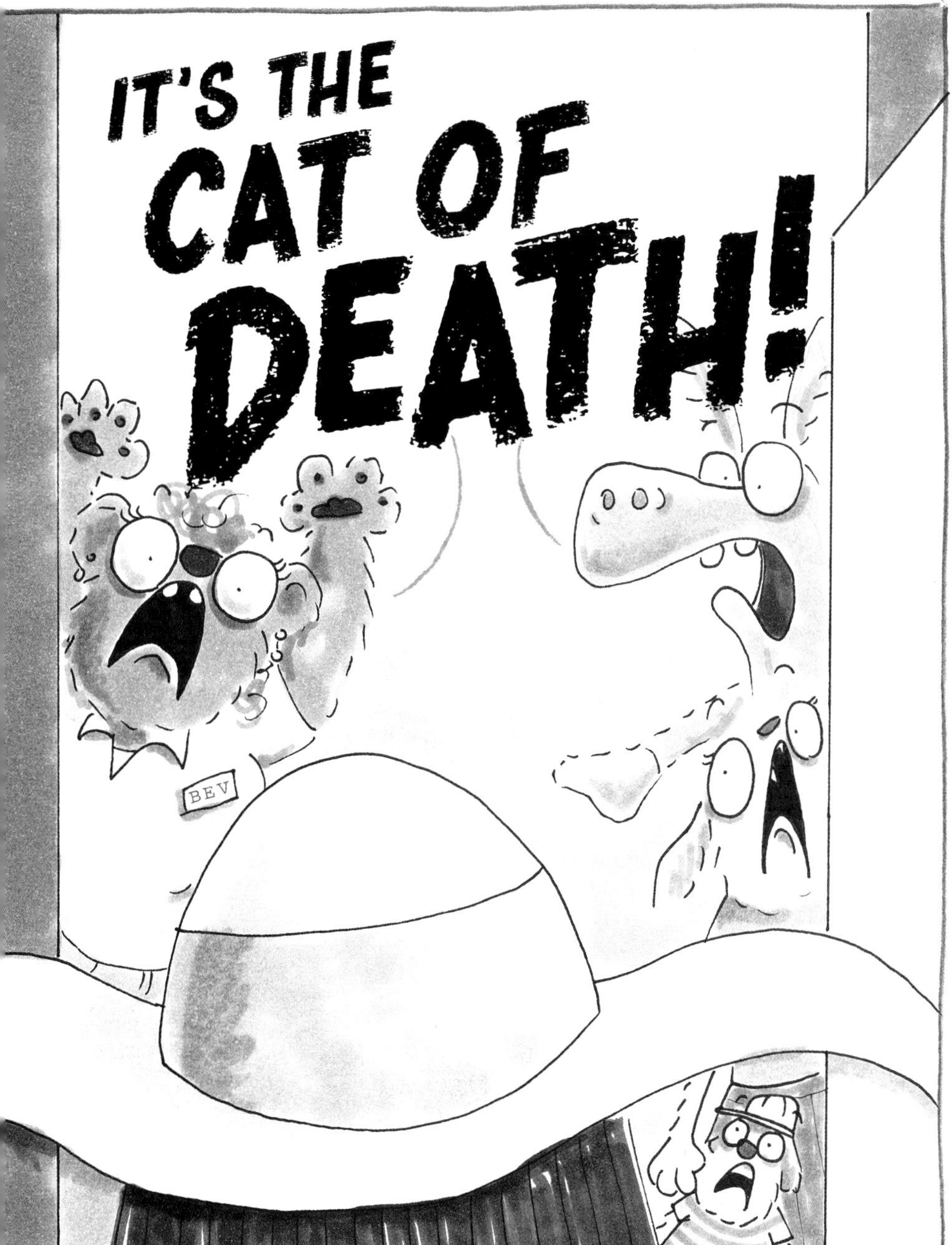
IT'S THE CAT OF DEATH!
BEV

Eight
FOLLOW THE SCORPION

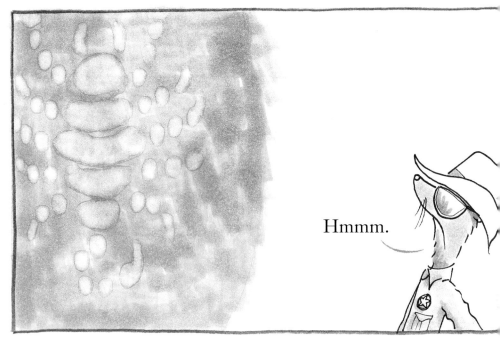

Wait!

Is that . . . ?!

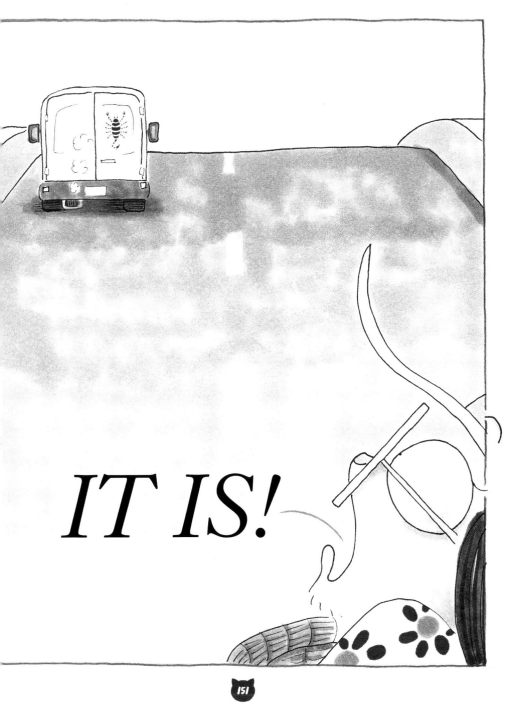

IT IS!

THAT'S IT!

VROOM!

NO!

WAIT!

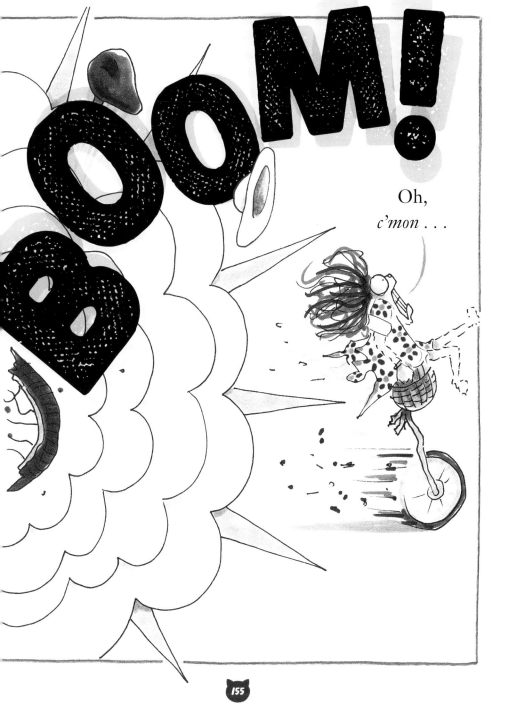

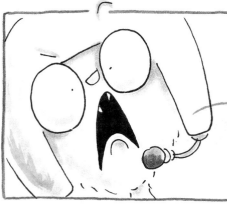

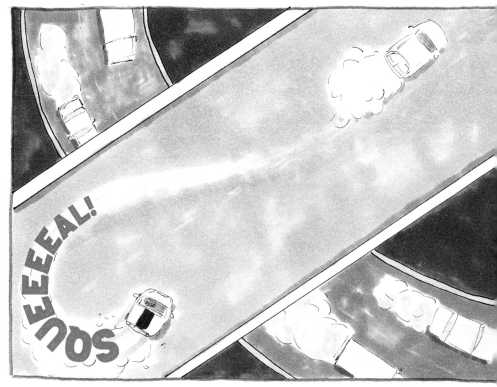

COME
BACK
HERE!

Nine
THE ABYSS

The pizza guy's
PHONE!

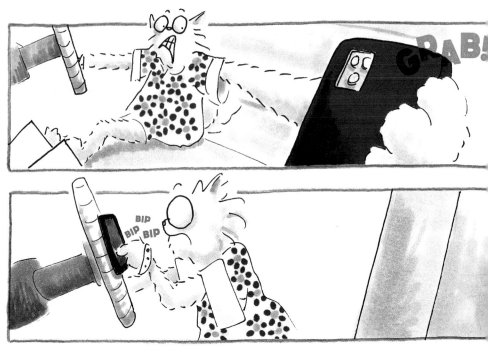

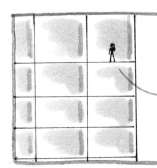

The internet is trying to eat you alive but *I won't let it.*

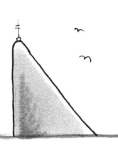

I want you to hear this -
**I BELIEVE YOU.
MY FAMILY
BELIEVES YOU . . .**

and we are going to do everything we can to show the world that

**YOU ARE
INNOCENT.**

And I don't want
to freak you out
or anything, but . . .

I think I love you.

Now . . .
WHAT CAN I DO
TO HELP?

Maybe just repeat
that last part again?

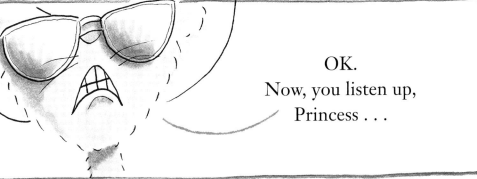

OK.
Now, you listen up,
Princess . . .

If you **COME ALONG QUIETLY...**

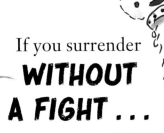

If you surrender **WITHOUT A FIGHT...**

I promise, I'll put in a **GOOD WORD FOR YOU.**

and we are going to do everything we can to show the world that

YOU ARE INNOCENT.

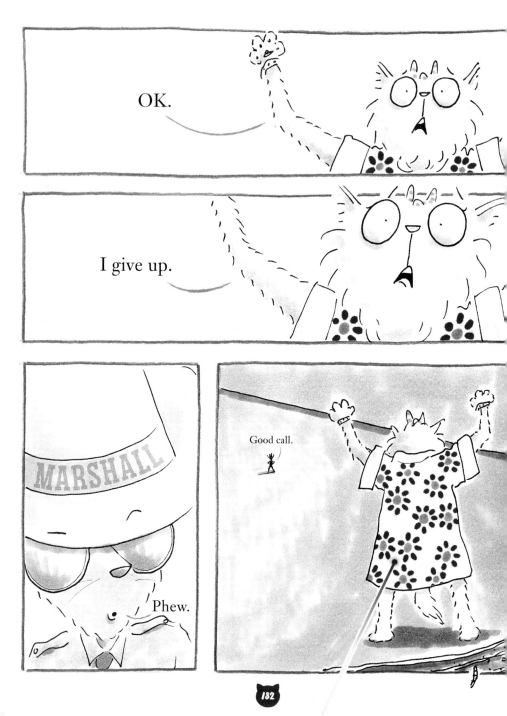

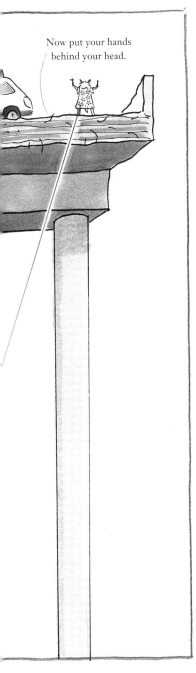

Now put your hands behind your head.

SHHHHMMM

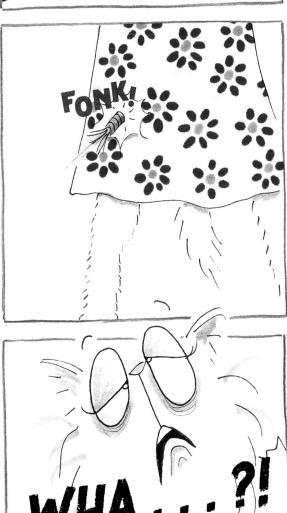

FONK!

WHA . . . . ?!

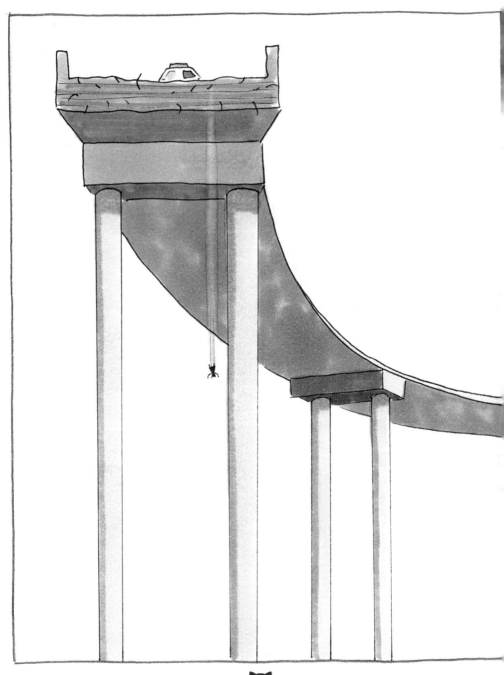

Ten

FOOF!

TO BE CONTINUED . . .

CAT on the RUN

EPISODE 2
COMING SOON!